Theory Paper Grade 7 2008 A

CW01023572

Duration 3 hours

Candidates should answer all FIVE questions.
Write your answers on this paper – no others will be accepted.
Answers must be written clearly and neatly – otherwise marks may be lost.

TOTAL MARKS
100

1 Indicate suitable chords for a continuo player by figuring the bass as necessary, *from the beginning of bar 5*, at the places marked ∗ in this passage. If you wish to use a $\frac{5}{3}$ chord, leave the space under the asterisk blank, but $\frac{5}{3}$ chords *must* be shown when used as part of a $\frac{6}{4}\frac{5}{3}$ progression or when chromatic alteration is required. All other chords should be indicated, as should any suspended dissonances.

15

Albinoni, Sonata in G minor, Op. 6 No. 2 (adapted)

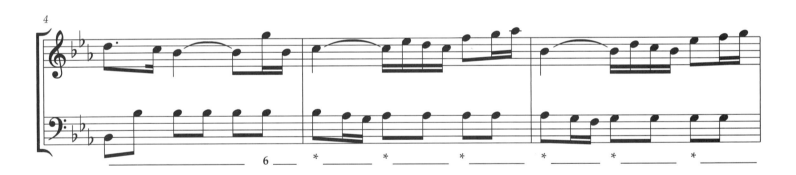

etc.

3

2 On the staves marked **A** below is an outline of a passage adapted from a minuet by J. L. Dussek, leaving out certain rests, passing notes and other notes of melodic decoration. The music on the staves marked **B** is what the composer actually wrote. Continuing in the same style, reconstruct the blank and partially completed bars.

3 EITHER

(a) Complete the oboe part in the following passage, which is adapted from a song by Beethoven. Phrase marks have been inserted above the oboe stave to indicate the structure you might use.

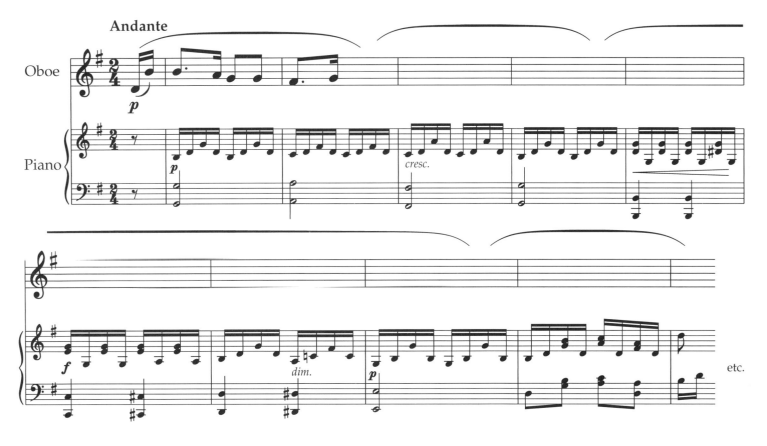

OR

(b) Compose a complete melody of not less than eight bars in length for unaccompanied trumpet (at concert pitch) or violin, based on the given opening. Write the complete melody on the staves below, include appropriate performance directions for the instrument of your choice and state below which it is.

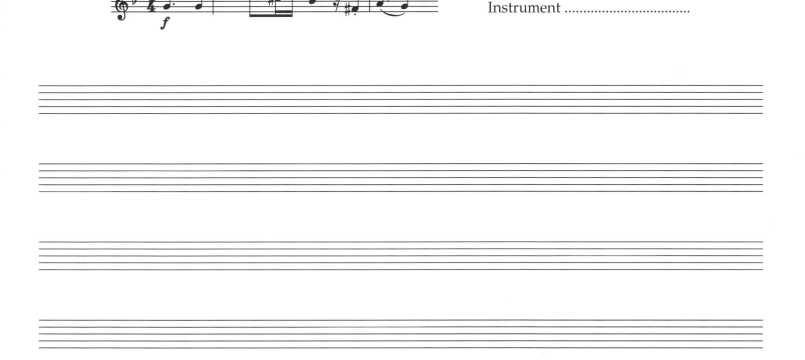

Instrument ....

4 Look at the extract printed opposite, which is the beginning of the third movement of a string quartet by Dvořák, and then answer the questions below.

(a) Give the meaning of **Lento e molto cantabile**. .... (3)

(b) Identify the chord marked ∗ in bar 14 by writing on the dotted lines below. Use either words or symbols. Indicate the position of the chord, whether it is major, minor, augmented or diminished, and name the prevailing key.

Chord .... Key .... (4)

(c) Complete the following statement:

The opening theme, played by the first violin in bars 1–4, is later repeated by the ....

.... in bars ...., two differences being ....

.... and

.... (4)

(d) Mark **clearly** on the score, using the appropriate capital letter for identification, one example of each of the following. Also give the bar number of each of your answers. The first answer is given.

A a melodic interval of a diminished 4th
in the first violin part (circle the notes concerned). Bar ...10....

B in bars 1–12, an example of syncopation. Bar .... (2)

C a place where the viola and cello sound two consecutive notes in unison. Bar(s) .... (2)

D in bars 1–8, a double stop that forms the harmonic interval of a perfect 4th. Bar .... (2)

E in bars 9–16, a note of anticipation in the
second violin part (circle the note concerned). Bar .... (2)

F a descending chromatic semitone in the
cello part (circle the notes concerned). Bar .... (2)

(e) Describe fully the numbered and bracketed harmonic intervals in the following bars:

1 (bar 7) .... (2)

2 (bar 12) .... (2)

5 Look at the extract printed on pages 9–10, which is from the second movement of d'Indy's Symphony No. 2, and then answer the questions below. [25]

(a) Give the meaning of:

en dehors (cor anglais, bar 1) .... (2)

en animant (bar 5) .... (2)

(b) (i) Write out the part for first clarinet in bars 2–3 as it would sound at concert pitch.

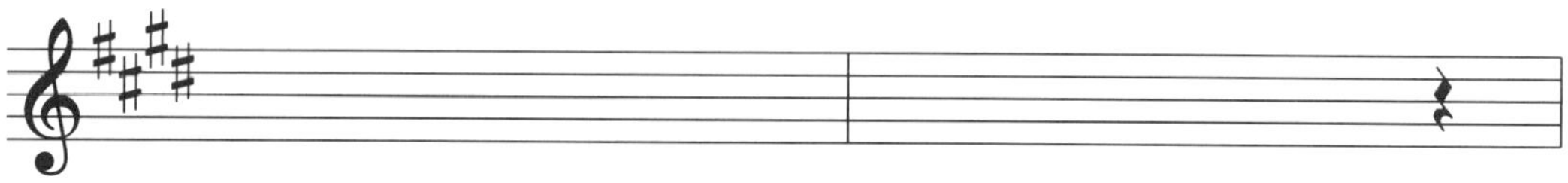

(3)

(ii) Using the blank staves at the foot of page 10, write out the parts for horns in bars 4–5 as they would sound at concert pitch. (5)

(c) Mark **clearly** on the score, using the appropriate capital letter for identification, one example of each of the following. Also give the bar number of each of your answers. The first answer is given.

A in a woodwind part, an instruction for both players to play the same line. Bar ....4....

B a harmonic interval of a diminished 4th *sounding* between two single-reed instruments (circle the notes concerned). Bar .... (2)

C a harmonic interval of a compound augmented 4th (augmented 11th) *sounding* between two double-reed instruments (circle the notes concerned). Bar .... (2)

(d) Complete the following statement:

The English name for the grosse caisse, an instrument which plays in an earlier movement of this work, is .... (2)

(e) Name three ways in which bars 5 and 6 prepare for a climax which occurs shortly after the extract ends.

1 .... (1)

2 .... (1)

3 .... (1)

(f) Answer TRUE or FALSE to each of the following statements:

(i) The only brass instruments playing in this extract are the horns. .... (2)

(ii) For the first three notes of bar 5, the first oboe and second clarinet sound an octave apart. .... (2)

8

Modérément lent (plus animé)

9

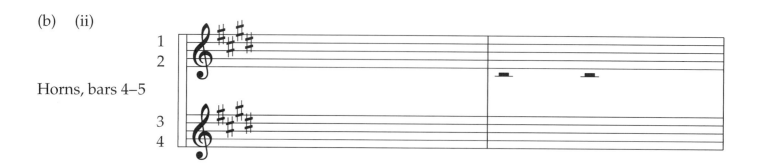

Horns, bars 4–5

Theory Paper Grade 7   2008   B

**DO NOT
PHOTOCOPY
© MUSIC**

Duration 3 hours

Candidates should answer all FIVE questions.
Write your answers on this paper – no others will be accepted.
Answers must be written clearly and neatly – otherwise marks may be lost.

TOTAL MARKS
100

1 Indicate suitable chords for a continuo player by figuring the bass as necessary, *from the beginning of bar 5*, at the places marked * in this passage. If you wish to use a $\frac{5}{3}$ chord, leave the space under the asterisk blank, but $\frac{5}{3}$ chords *must* be shown when used as part of a $\frac{6}{4}\frac{5}{3}$ progression or when chromatic alteration is required. All other chords should be indicated, as should any suspended dissonances.

15

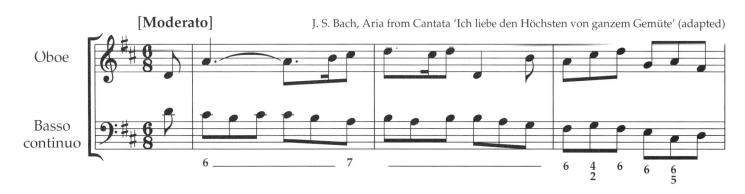

2 On the staves marked **A** below is an outline of part of a chorale harmonized by J. S. Bach, leaving out certain suspensions, passing notes and other notes of melodic decoration. The music on the staves marked **B** is what the composer actually wrote. Continuing in the same style, reconstruct the blank and partially completed bars.

3 EITHER

(a) Complete the violin part in the following passage, which is adapted from a song by Brahms. Phrase marks have been inserted above the violin stave to indicate the structure you might use.

OR

(b) Compose a complete melody of eight bars in length for unaccompanied cello or bassoon. Form your melody from the chord progression below, using the chords for each bar, together with any diatonic or chromatic decorations you consider appropriate. You may use the given opening or not, as you prefer. Write the complete melody on the staves below, include appropriate performance directions for the instrument of your choice and state below which it is.

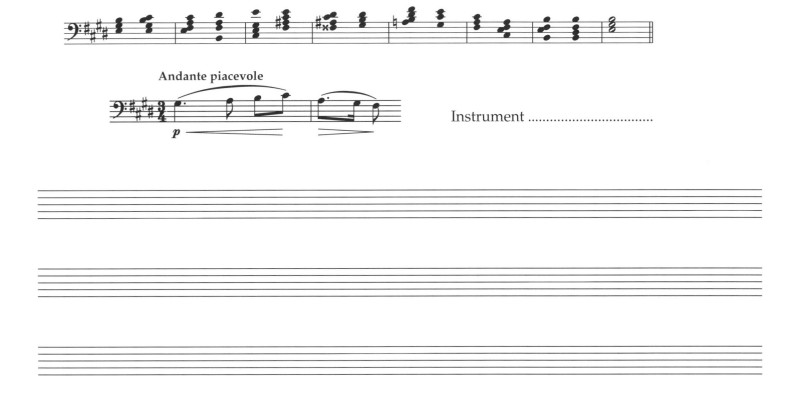

Instrument ....

Andante con espressione

etc.

4 Look at the extract printed opposite and then answer the questions below.

(a) Complete the following statements:

    (i) The opening two-bar phrase of the right-hand part next occurs in bars ...., two   (1)
        differences being:

        1   ....   (1)

        2   ....   (1)

    (ii) Later, the composer twice uses a melodically decorated version of the opening phrase,

        first in bars .... and then in bars ....   (4)

(b) Identify the chord marked ＊ in bar 9 by writing on the dotted lines below. Use either words
    or symbols. Indicate the position of the chord, whether it is major, minor, augmented or
    diminished, and name the prevailing key.

    Chord   ....   Key ....   (4)

(c) Write out in full the right-hand part of bar 22 as you think it should be played.

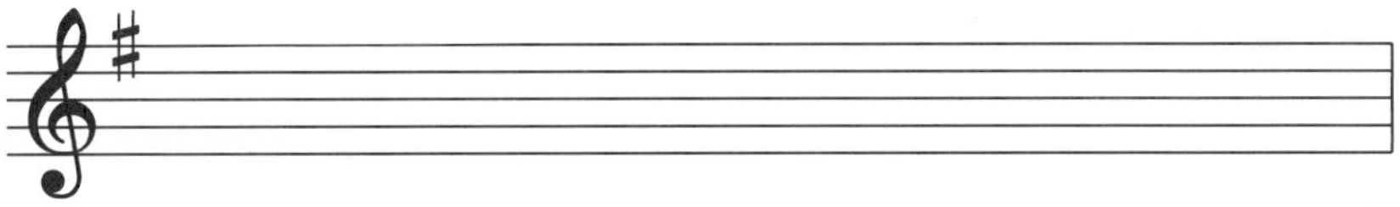

    (3)

(d) Mark **clearly** on the score, using the appropriate capital letter for identification, one example
    of each of the following. Also give the bar number(s) of each of your answers. The first answer
    is given.

    In bars 1–14

    A   a harmonic interval of a major 6th sounding
        between two left-hand notes (circle the notes concerned).   Bar ....8....

    B   a dominant 7th in third inversion (V^7d) in the subdominant key.   Bar ....   (2)

    C   a pair of upward-resolving appoggiaturas
        a major 10th apart (circle the notes concerned).   Bar ....   (2)

    D   a chromatic lower auxiliary note in the right-hand part.   Bar ....   (2)

    From bar 15 onwards

    E   a dominant inner (middle) pedal (not sustained) lasting for three bars.   Bars ....   (2)

    F   use of syncopation.   Bar(s) ....   (2)

(e) From the list below, underline one period during which you think the piece was written.

            1700–1800   1800–1900   1900–2000   (1)

5 Look at the extract printed on pages 17–18 and then answer the questions below. | 25 |

(a) (i) Give the meaning of *affret.* (affrettando) (first violins, bar 5).

.... (2)

(ii) Two instruments not playing in this extract are the gran cassa and the piatti. The English names for these instruments are:

Gran Cassa ....   (2)

Piatti ....   (2)

(b) (i) Write out the parts for first and second clarinets in bars 1–4 as they would sound at concert pitch.

(4)

(ii) Write out the parts for horns in bars 7–9 as they would sound at concert pitch and using the given clefs.

(4)

(c) Complete the following statements:

(i) On the first beat of bar 5, the instruments that play the *lowest* sounding note are the

..............................., the .... and the ....   (3)

(ii) In bar 10, the instruments that play in unison with the cellos are the ....,

the .... and the ....   (3)

(d) Describe fully the numbered and bracketed harmonic intervals sounding on the first beat of the following bars:

1 bar 2 (first bassoon and second oboe) ....   (2)

2 bar 5 (second bassoon and first flute) ....   (2)

(e) From the list below, underline the name of the most likely composer of this extract.

Beethoven   Ravel   Elgar   Rossini   (1)

16

Theory Paper Grade 7   2008   C

Duration 3 hours

Candidates should answer all FIVE questions.
Write your answers on this paper – no others will be accepted.
Answers must be written clearly and neatly – otherwise marks may be lost.

TOTAL MARKS
100

1   Indicate suitable chords for a continuo player by figuring the bass as necessary, *from the beginning of bar 5*, at the places marked ＊ in this passage. If you wish to use a $\frac{5}{3}$ chord, leave the space under the asterisk blank, but $\frac{5}{3}$ chords *must* be shown when used as part of a $\frac{6}{4}\frac{5}{3}$ progression or when chromatic alteration is required. All other chords should be indicated, as should any suspended dissonances.

15

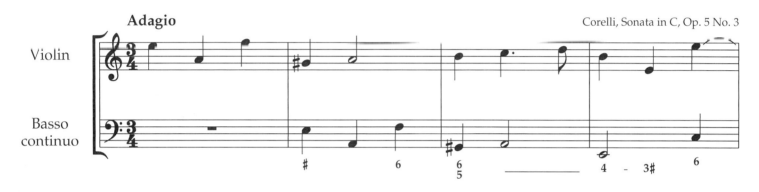

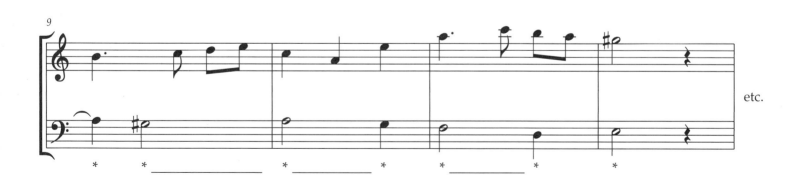

2 On the staves marked **A** below is an outline of part of a chorale harmonized by J. S. Bach,  leaving out certain suspensions, passing notes and other notes of melodic decoration. The music on the staves marked **B** is what the composer actually wrote. Continuing in the same style, reconstruct the blank and partially completed bars.

3 EITHER

(a) Complete the flute part in the following passage, which is adapted from a song by Mendelssohn. Phrase marks have been inserted above the flute stave to indicate the structure you might use.

OR

(b) Compose a complete melody of not less than eight bars in length for unaccompanied trumpet (at concert pitch) or oboe, based on the given opening. Write the complete melody on the staves below, include appropriate performance directions for the instrument of your choice and state below which it is.

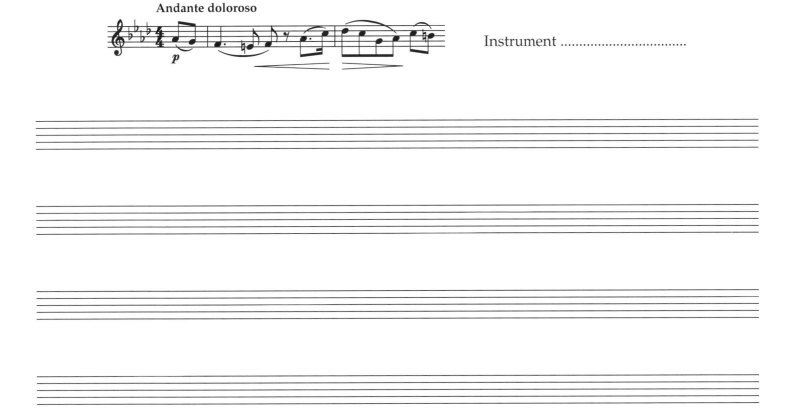

Instrument ....

4 Look at the extract printed opposite, which is from a Lied by Schubert, and then answer the questions below.

[25]

(a) Mark **clearly** on the score, using the appropriate capital letter for identification, one example of each of the following. Also give the bar number(s) of each of your answers. The first answer is given.

A a diminished 7th chord in D minor. Bar ......1......

B a complete bar where the vocal part is lower than the top line of the right-hand piano part. Bar .... (2)

C in bars 1–9, an unaccented passing note in the vocal part over a subdominant chord in second inversion (IVc) in the piano part (circle the note concerned). Bar .... (2)

D a perfect cadence in the dominant key. Bars .... (2)

E an upper auxiliary note in the vocal part (circle the note concerned). Bar .... (2)

F an appoggiatura in the left-hand piano part (circle the note concerned). Bar .... (2)

(b) Identify the chords marked * in bars 1 and 10 by writing on the dotted lines below. Use either words or symbols. Indicate the position of each chord, show whether it is major, minor, augmented or diminished and name the prevailing key in bar 10.

Bar 1 .... Key: G minor (3)

Bar 10 .... Key: .... (4)

(c) Rewrite bars 3–4 of the vocal part (*without the text but including the rests at the start of bar 3*) in compound time but without changing the rhythmic effect. Remember to include the new time signature.

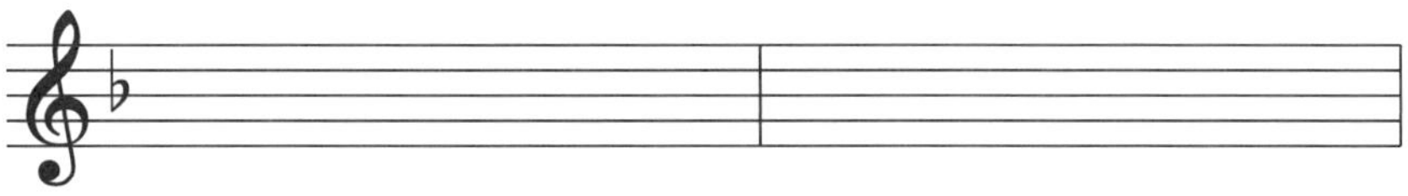

(4)

(d) Describe fully the numbered and bracketed harmonic intervals in the following bars:

1 bar 7, final quaver (voice and left-hand piano part) .... (2)

2 bar 11, final quaver (top right-hand and top left-hand piano part) .... (2)

5 Look at the extract printed on pages 25–26, which is from the fifth movement of Skryabin's Symphony No. 2, and then answer the questions below.

(a) Give the meaning of:

scherzando (e.g. viola, bar 1) .... (2)

∨ (e.g. first violin, bar 1) .... (2)

div. (e.g. second violin, bar 1) .... (2)

(b) (i) Write out the parts for horns in bars 1–2 as they would sound at concert pitch.

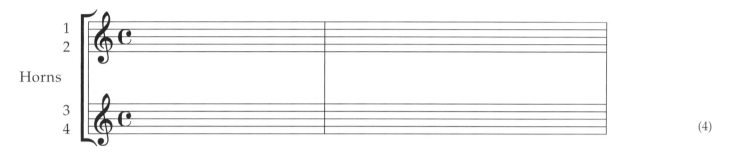

(4)

(ii) Using the blank staves at the foot of page 26, write out the parts for clarinets in bars 7–8 as they would sound at concert pitch. (4)

(c) Describe fully the numbered and bracketed harmonic intervals *sounding* in the following bars:

1 bar 5, first beat (third clarinet and flutes) .... (2)

2 bar 7, first beat (second violins and second horn) .... (2)

(d) Complete the following statements:

(i) The opening two-bar phrase played by the first violins is repeated in bars .... by

the .... at the interval of a(n) .... (3)

(ii) To make a complete dominant 7th (V^7) chord, the violas in bar 1 would need to add the

note .... to the triplet semiquavers. (2)

(iii) The instruments playing in unison with the first bassoon in bar 8 are

the .... (2)

25

(b) (ii)

Clarinets, bars 7–8

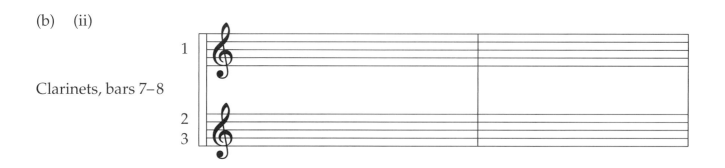

Theory Paper Grade 7   2008   S

TOTAL MARKS
100

Duration 3 hours

Candidates should answer all FIVE questions.
Write your answers on this paper – no others will be accepted.
Answers must be written clearly and neatly – otherwise marks may be lost.

1 Indicate suitable chords for a continuo player by figuring the bass as necessary, *from the third beat of bar 3*, at the places marked ∗ in this passage. If you wish to use a $\frac{5}{3}$ chord, leave the space under the asterisk blank, but $\frac{5}{3}$ chords *must* be shown when used as part of a $\frac{6}{4}\frac{5}{3}$ progression or when chromatic alteration is required. All other chords should be indicated, as should any suspended dissonances.

15

Corelli, Sonata a tre, Op. 3 No. 10 (adapted)

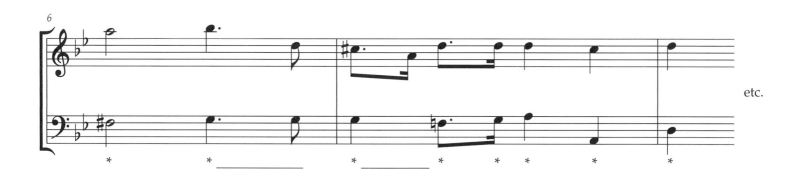

27

2 On the staves marked **A** below is an outline of a passage adapted from a sonatina by 15 Kuhlau, leaving out certain rests, passing notes and other notes of melodic decoration. The music on the staves marked **B** is what the composer actually wrote. Continuing in the same style, reconstruct the blank and partially completed bars.

3 EITHER

    (a) Complete the oboe part in the following passage, which is adapted from a nocturne for violin by N. Burgmüller. Phrase marks have been inserted above the oboe stave to indicate the structure you might use.

OR

    (b) Compose a complete melody of not less than eight bars in length for unaccompanied trombone or bassoon, based on the given opening. Write the complete melody on the staves below, include appropriate performance directions for the instrument of your choice and state below which it is.

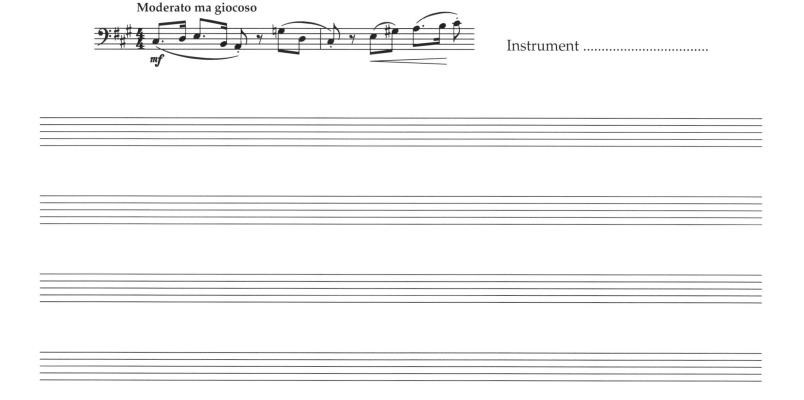

Instrument ....

4 Look at the extract printed opposite, which is from M. Clementi's Sonata Op. 7 No. 3, and then answer the questions below.

25

(a) Identify the chord formed from the shaded notes marked ∗ in bar 7 by writing on the dotted lines below. Use either words or symbols. Indicate the position of the chord, whether it is major, minor, augmented or diminished, and name the prevailing key.

Chord .... Key .... (4)

(b) Give the full names of the notes of melodic decoration (e.g. changing note) marked **X** in bars 2, 12 and 18.

Bar 2 (left-hand) .... (2)

Bar 12 (left-hand) .... (2)

Bar 18 (right-hand) .... (2)

(c) Write out in full the right-hand part of bar 4 as you think it should be played.

(3)

(d) Mark **clearly** on the score, using the appropriate capital letter for identification, one example of each of the following. Also give the bar number(s) of each of your answers. The first answer is given.

A   a tonic pedal lasting for three bars (mark └──**A**──┘ under the bars). Bars ....1–3........

B   from bar 13 onwards, a melodic interval of a
diminished 5th in the right-hand part (circle the notes concerned). Bar .... (2)

C   a diminished 7th chord in second inversion in the relative minor key. Bar .... (2)

D   in bars 1–12, a one-bar sequence in the right-hand part over a dominant pedal. Bar .... (2)

E   from bar 13 onwards, a harmonic interval of an
augmented 2nd in the left-hand part (circle the notes concerned). Bar .... (2)

(e) Answer TRUE or FALSE to the following statements:

(i)   There is a perfect cadence in the dominant key in bars 19–20. .... (2)

(ii) The written-out ornament in bar 10 is a trill. .... (2)

5 Look at the extract printed on pages 33–34 and then answer the questions below. 〔25〕

(a) Give the meaning of:

Lebhaft, doch nicht schnell .... (4)

unis. (bar 13, cellos) .... (2)

(b) Write out the parts for clarinets and horns in bars 2–3 as they would sound at concert pitch and using the given clefs.

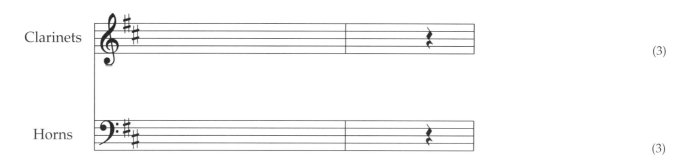

Clarinets (3)

Horns (3)

(c) Name one similarity and one difference between the oboe parts of bars 6–7 and 11–12.

Similarity: .... (2)

Difference: .... (2)

(d) Mark **clearly** on the score, using the appropriate capital letter for identification, one example of each of the following. Also give the bar number(s) of each of your answers. The first answer is given.

A   an example of syncopation in the solo violin part. Bar ....$\overset{4}{....}$...

B   a bar where the first and second violins play
    the same notes as the first and second oboes. Bar .... (2)

C   a double stop in the solo violin part. Bar .... (2)

D   a chord of a diminished 7th in the strings. Bar .... (2)

E   a melodic interval of a compound diminished 4th
    (diminished 11th) in the solo violin part (circle the notes concerned). Bars .... (2)

(e) From the list below, underline the name of the most likely composer of this extract.

      Bach   Schumann   Shostakovich   Bartók (1)

etc.

Theory of Music Exams Model Answers, 2008 are now available from your usual retailer.

Grade 1   978-1-86096-981-2
Grade 2   978-1-86096-982-9
Grade 3   978-1-86096-983-6
Grade 4   978-1-86096-984-3
Grade 5   978-1-86096-985-0
Grade 6   978-1-86096-986-7
Grade 7   978-1-86096-987-4
Grade 8   978-1-86096-988-1

Other music theory publications from ABRSM Publishing include:

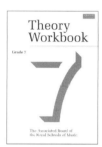

Theory Workbooks
Grades 6 to 8 (separately)
by Anna Butterworth, Anthony Crossland,
Terence Greaves and Michael Jacques

Music Theory in Practice
Grades 1 to 5 (separately)
by Eric Taylor

Grades 6 to 8 (separately)
by Peter Aston & Julian Webb

The AB Guide to Music Theory
Parts I and II
by Eric Taylor

Harmony in Practice
by Anna Butterworth

The Associated Board of
the Royal Schools of Music
(Publishing) Limited

24 Portland Place
London W1B 1LU
United Kingdom

www.abrsmpublishing.com

ISBN 978-1-86096-967-6

PAUL'S
£ 3.50

9 781860 969676